What others are saying about Chris Widener...

"Chris was very challenging and enriching. The leadership principles that he spoke on were at the very core of what we are trying to accomplish here on the HBS campus. Chris taught us the tenets of true leadership and how to immediately apply those truths in our own leadership situation. I would encourage everyone to learn from Chris Widener." -- John Lunde, Harvard Business School, Student Leader, MBA

*"I have spoken to more than 3,000 audiences and ' ___ ' you that Chris Widener is one of the best speakers i ___ v. He has wonderful content -- extremely motiv ___ he is sharp, he is quick and to the point. Y ___ * -- Brian Tracy, author of Eat That Fro*

"Our people loved Chris and lov ___ extremely helpful and challengin ___ __ I highly recommend him!" -- Phil Castillo, D ___ ern Channels, Cisco Systems

"Chris Widener has the talent, the articulation, the message, the presence, the ability! Chris Widener is one of the brand new top stars on the International platform speaking circuit today." -- Denis Waitley, author of Seeds of Greatness

"Chris Widener is a powerful presenter, a quick wit, and a home run every time. He definitely challenges you to the next level in life and work." -- Kevin Mather, CFO, Seattle Mariners Baseball Team

"Chris Widener is the leader of a new generation of personal development and leadership experts. He lives and breathes the strategies and tools he shares with millions around the globe. Chris' content is rich and practical, and his style is dynamic and engaging! If you want to see real change in your life, or the life of your organization, connect with Chris Widener." -- Jim Rohn, author of The Five Major Pieces to the Life Puzzle

THE IMAGE

by Chris Widener

A Novel about God, Success, and Business

Published by
Chris Widener International and SUCCESS
www.ChrisWidener.com
www.SUCCESS.com

Distributed by
SUCCESS
5800 Democracy Drive, Suite 100
Plano, Texas 75024

The Image / by Chris Widener

ISBN: 0-9726266-9-7 (Paperback)

Printed in The United States of America

THE IMAGE

Contents

Dedication

The Image is dedicated to the tens of millions of Christian business people who desire to be successful both spiritually and in business! Go for it - you are making a difference!

Chris Widener

Foreword

As a leader in my company and in an industry that relies greatly on personal growth, I am bombarded on a daily basis with books and articles from various success coaches and authors. On one such day last year, Loraine Grover, one of my business partners from Seattle sent me Chris Widener's book *The Angel Inside.* To be honest, I set it in my "to read" file, and didn't look at it again. A few months later, I heard that Chris was graciously opening his home in Seattle for Loraine, a member of his church, to host a celebration party that leaders in our company host when others reach the VP level of our business.

When I drove up to this beautiful home, and met Chris and his lovely wife and children, I knew they were very special. I was amazed as this young man began to speak, and poured out incredible wisdom beyond his years. The next afternoon, as I rode the ferry boat to visit my son on Orcas Island, I devoured *The Angel Inside.* I literally could not put it down. It touched me just as the early books of Og Mandino did early in my career. Chris has an incredible gift of weaving time tested success principles in a compelling story. As I write this, the top leaders in our business just returned from Florence, Italy, where we were all able to view Michelangelo's *"The David"* from Chris's perspective, because I had given them *The Angel Inside* before our trip!

Chris' next book *Twelve Pillars*, co-written with personal development legend Jim Rohn, made just as big of an impression on me and my team. We quickly saw a classic series developing!

Then Chris sent me a preview copy of the manuscript for *The Image.* I'm not sure if it's because the main character of this book, Susan, is a woman, but this is the one that hit closest to home. I wondered how these books could keep getting better and better! The principles Chris talks about in *The Image* are principles I have had to learn to get me where I am today, and are key for anyone who wants to achieve success in business.

I grew up in a loving, close-knit, blue collar family from Wisconsin, yet we had very few dreams, hopes, or desires beyond what everyone else was doing. It was the *status quo.* Success in my world meant trading hours for dollars, and not rising above my upbringing. With no college education, I excelled at swimming, and eventually became a swimming coach. That is where I started to study success and coaching principles. In my early twenties, I was fortunate to be exposed to incredible mentors and teachers because of my involvement in an industry that places a very high value on personal growth and development.

In my journey, I found myself asking many of the same questions that the young woman, Kate, asks in her quest to find her purpose in *The Image.*

In John 10:10, it says, *I have come that they may have life, and have it to be full.* In other words, Christ wants us to have a life of abundance. If our tank is full, it will overflow out of us, and spill onto others. As the president of my company often says, "You can do so much more to help people when you have abundance, than when you don't."

The sooner you can take in these incredible success principles, and apply them in your life, the sooner you can share them with others. That is where the true gift lies. You will have more passion for what you do when you come from a place of serving and giving than you could ever experience from receiving. Now that I have reached incredible success in my own career, earning more in a week than I could imagine in a year, I am amazed at my passion and desire to be a giver and teacher of these success principles. The motivation is no longer *money based*, but rather, *contribution based.*

It's never too late to be the person you always wanted to be, and it's never too late to inspire others to do the same. We all have a gift, and a purpose. Contrary to the current culture that says, *"It's all about ME"*, we are here for a reason beyond ourselves. We are designed to learn, love, and share our gifts with others. Our destiny from God is greatness, not simply in what we achieve, but in how we serve when we achieve it. Ours can be lives of both spirituality *and* abundance!

I can promise you, that once you begin to read *The Image* you will not be able to put it down. Like the movie, *Pay it Forward,* enjoy it, but pass it on to inspire others. You have just lit your own fire. Now pass on your torch, and fuel the flame to ignite others! You *can* make a difference, and with God's strength, you are well on your way!

Now, no pressure Chris, but how can you top *"The Image"?*

Donna Johnson

1

The Bus Ride

"I am basically struggling with how my work – and what I want to accomplish in life – goes together with my Christian faith."

It's funny what can come from a "chance" meeting.

Kate Miller was riding the Metro Bus into Seattle from her condo in a suburb east of Seattle for at least the 1,000th time. Every day for the past five years she had gotten up and commuted to her office in Seattle to engage in the wheels of commerce. Right out of business school she had secured a job with a prestigious firm that handled high level business transactions and business exchanges. Although she enjoyed it, something held her back. Something kept her from living *fully* engaged in the process.

She sat on the bus as it came to a stop at the Eastgate Park and Ride, watching as a number of people got on and took their seats. She recognized the same people, even though she had never really spoken to any of them before. Then one woman, about fifty-five, got on who caught her eye. She looked familiar for some reason. Maybe a local celebrity? But why would she be riding the bus? She was very well put together--hair perfect, nails done, like she walked right out of a Talbot's Catalogue-- certainly not the look of most people who ride the bus!

The woman walked back as Kate watched, and then she stopped right in front of Kate.

"Would you mind if I sit next to you?" she asked.

"Oh, of course," Kate responded, moving her newspaper out of the seat to make way for the older woman.

"Thank you," she said, the model of decorum. She placed her purse on her lap and extended her hand. "I am Susan Hart. How are you?"

Kate took her hand and shook it. "I'm fine, thank you. My name is Kate. Kate Miller."

"Nice to meet you, Kate."

"I've never seen you on the bus before. Are you new here?"

"No, I just had to leave my car in the shop. They didn't have any loaner cars and my husband is out of town, so I decided to take the bus."

Kate just smiled. She wondered what kind of car a woman like Susan Hart drove. She concluded Susan drove a Jaguar. "What kind of car do you drive?" she asked.

"I have a Bentley Coupe," Susan replied.

Wow. Under-guessed that one, didn't you?, Kate thought. There was a bit of uncomfortable silence as Kate pondered the woman who sat next to her – the woman who drives a car worth more than her studio condo.

They sat quietly next to each other for a few moments. The bus pulled back onto the street and was on its way before Susan asked what Kate did for a living.

"Well, believe it or not, today is my last day at a job I have had for five years. I am in business brokering, basically. I work at Smith, Allen and Jones."

"Oh, I am familiar with them. Why are you leaving that position?"

"Well, I like it, but I feel a little unfulfilled. I have a bunch of money saved up, so I am going to take a few months off, think about what I want to do and then make a career move."

"That sounds like a great idea. What kinds of things are you going to think about?"

Kate had given a lot of thought about what she wanted to think about. She knew the answers that she would be looking for. Little did she know that the answers had come looking for her in the form of Susan Hart. "I am basically struggling with how my work – and what I want to accomplish in life – goes together with my Christian faith." Kate didn't know where Susan stood on issues of faith but figured she would cut to the chase.

"Yes, the idea of Christianity and the workplace is a big one," Susan said.

"Are you a Christian?"

"Certainly. I have been since the seventies. I grew up in a great home, but one where we didn't talk much about God or Christianity. In college, I went on a retreat with a friend of mine and became a follower of Christ. Changed my life ever since."

"That's great."

"It is. It has made a real difference, and I understand what you may be going through."

Kate looked out the bus window at Lake Washington as they drove the last part of the I-90 floating bridge and entered into the tunnel that would take them into Seattle.

"What exactly are you thinking about in relation to faith?" Susan asked.

"Well, I guess how I can be successful, make a lot of money, achieve all of my dreams and still be a Christian."

"You think that you can't do all of those things and still be a Christian?"

"I don't know. I mean, think of all the sermons you've heard on 'blessed are the poor,' 'be humble,' 'don't long for things of this world.' It just doesn't add up."

The bus was now proceeding up Fourth Avenue and Susan was reaching into her purse for a business card. As the bus came to a stop, she handed the card to Kate and told her to call her later today. Susan invited Kate over to her office to talk further. "This is my stop, so I have to get off. Call me. I think I can help you."

"I will," Kate said. With that, Susan exited the bus and walked toward a glistening glass building. Kate watched her enter the building that had an ornate sign above the entrance: *World Headquarters of The Hart Companies.*

The Hart Companies. I know that name.... No wonder she's so wealthy – she has a fifty-story building with her name on it.

16

2

Meeting Susan Hart

"I have a very unique way I am thinking of that will help you get to those answers."

About ten a.m. the next morning – after sleeping in for the first time in what seemed like forever – Kate poured herself a cup of coffee and held Susan Hart's business card in her hand.

Susan Hart
Chief Executive Officer
The Hart Companies

Offices in 20 Countries. That's some business.

Kate decided to call Susan and take her up on her offer of getting together. At first glance, Susan seemed exactly like the type of person that Kate would like to become someday. She was a successful woman, and a Christian. That intrigued Kate and she wanted to know more.

She picked up the phone and dialed the number that said it was a direct dial to Susan. After two rings the phone picked up and Kate recognized Susan's voice.

"Hello. Susan Hart."

"Susan, this is Kate Miller. We met on the bus yesterday."

"Yes, Kate. I am so glad that you called."

"I didn't expect to get to you directly. I figured you would have an administrative assistant or something."

"Oh, I do, but I have some cards made up that have my direct dial number on them. They are for special people like you, Kate."

"Well, that is so nice of you. I guess I wanted to call and see if you are still up for meeting with me and helping me navigate the waters we talked about yesterday."

"Certainly, Kate. I would love to. Hold on for a moment and let me look at my calendar for the rest of the week. Okay, I have a lunch available the day after tomorrow. Can you do that?"

"I sure can. I am available for lunch every day now for the foreseeable future. Are you sure this isn't an intrusion?"

"Certainly not. I am looking forward to it. I have asked many of the same questions and if I can help you get to the answers faster than I did, I would be very pleased. And… I have a very unique way I am thinking of that will help you get to those answers. I can't wait to tell you about it."

"That sounds great. What time should I come?"

"How about 11:30? I get hungry early. My office is on the top floor of the building I went into yesterday."

"Okay. Great. I will be there. Thanks so much, Susan."

"My pleasure, Kate. I look forward to it.

3

The Theology of the Image

"There is always a purpose for what God gives us."

The next day, Kate put on her nicest business suit and made the trek to downtown Seattle and the World Headquarters of the Hart Companies. At precisely 11:27 a.m. she pushed the button in the elevator that would take her to Susan's office on the top floor. Or so she thought...

In fact, when the elevator doors opened up, Kate realized it wasn't that Susan's office was *on* the top floor as much as that it *was* the top floor. Just out of the elevator was a reception desk but other than that, the entire floor was wide open. The whole floor was literally one big office. It was divided by furniture that made up different areas of the office, but it was one large office. There was an area that was obviously where Susan did her work with a large desk, a return and a credenza. There was a living room style area. There was an area that looked like a library, with bookshelves and couches. There was a dining area – which totally surprised Kate – that had a cherry table that sat at least 16 people. There was a conference area that had a table that held at least 30 people, and lastly, there was a multi-media area where one could watch video.

"You must be Kate," the young woman behind the reception desk said. "Mrs. Hart is expecting you."

"Yes, that's me."

"She asked me to just have you go over to her desk. Her call will be over in a minute."

Kate could see that Susan was standing behind her desk, talking into a wireless headset. Kate sat in a chair and waited just a few minutes before Susan ended her call.

"Kate, you look fabulous today!" Susan exclaimed.

"Oh, thank you," Kate said. "You look great, too."

"Well, us two great looking ladies are going to eat at the Georgian Room at the Fairmont Olympic Hotel. Do you mind?"

"That sounds fantastic. I would love to."

"Let's go then!"

The two women rode the elevator down to the lobby and then Susan took her to a special elevator that required a key that took them down to a private parking garage where Susan kept her newly repaired Bentley GT.

"I love this car," she said as she hit the door unlock button on her remote." It just had a little tweak they had to do to the electronics yesterday, but a car like this needs all day to do it. Runs great now!"

Kate and Susan climbed into the nicest car Kate had ever been in. It was the ultimate in beauty – at least as far as cars go. It rode so smooth. They made their way north a few blocks and pulled into the valet parking at the Fairmont Olympic Hotel. As they got out, the valet welcomed them. "Good to see you again, Mrs. Hart."

"Thank you, Robert. Nice to see you, too."

Susan and Kate walked up to the Georgian Room and were promptly seated by the host. "This is so elegant," Kate said.

"I know. There are so many fabulous restaurants in Seattle, but I always love coming to this place. I thought we would eat in my office, but our chef called in sick today, so here we are."

The women looked over the menu and made their choices known to their server and were now waiting for their lunch to arrive when Susan opened the conversation to the topic of the day: Faith and the Workplace.

"So Kate, I have been thinking about a way that I could help you think through some of the issues that you are struggling with. I know that I was at one time struggling with the same things until I realized a very important concept that I will tell you about in a few minutes. I always knew that I *could* accomplish anything I wanted to, I just didn't know if I *should*."

"That is exactly what I am struggling with. Is being ambitious okay? Is setting goals and having dreams okay? Is self-improvement alright for Christians? That kind of thing."

"Yes, exactly the things that I had to answer for myself. Twenty-five years ago I was making a decent living but I knew in my heart – deep in my heart – that God had a plan for me. A *big* plan. But I couldn't get over the perceptions I had of what Christianity was. I felt like I needed to take a vow of poverty or something in order to become spiritual or maintain my spirituality. But then two things happened."

"What were they?" Kate asked.

"First, I started meeting people who were both successful as well as deeply spiritual. They did extraordinary things with their lives and careers but all the while kept themselves in step with their Christian faith. They realized that their Christianity was the foundation for what they did in the workplace."

"And what was the second?"

"The second totally transformed how I look at life. It is what I call the Theology of the Image."

"The Theology of the Image? I don't get it."

The waiter returned and poured more water into their glasses before Susan continued.

"The Theology of the Image is basically this: We humans are created in the image of God. The Bible says that. All people. We are to be a reflection of the image of God in all that we are, and all that we do."

"Okay, I get that. But how does that translate?"

"It translates like this, Kate. We are made in His image. We are a reflection of His life. When we see what God is like, we see what we are to be like. We are called to live in this life so that we look like Him in who we are and what we do. That simple truth has transformed my life."

"How so?" Kate still didn't quite get it.

"In everything I do, and in all that I want to be, I ask myself whether or not it would be a reflection of having been made in His image. If my answer to that is yes, it does, then it is settled in my mind and I feel free to become that type of person or pursue that course of action. The key to life is to be constantly involved in your own personal transformation."

"Personal transformation? Into what?"

"Into a person that more wholly reflects the image of God."

"I get it," Kate said enthusiastically.

"You see Kate, there are many well-meaning people who take one side of what the bible teaches – and don't get me wrong, there are plenty of warnings against the extremes of ambition, wealth and power – but they forget that God Himself is ambitious, wealthy, and powerful. The key is to make sure that we are acting as that expression of His life, rather than the distorted perversion of that image that causes us to go awry."

"What do you mean by 'distorted perversion'?"

"For example, wealth. It is fine to be wealthy. Wealthy people who are transformed by God can do great things as stewards of that wealth. Wealthy people who are not transformed and living as a reflection of His life, can do great damage with their wealth. At the very best, they miss tremendous opportunities for generosity because they live in self-indulgence and absorption. There is always a purpose for what God gives us."

"Like what?" Kate asked.

"In Deuteronomy, Chapter Eight, God told the Israelites that it is God who gives them the power to get wealth – and this is important – for the establishment of His covenant. Not for their own enjoyment, though wealthy people can enjoy their wealth, but for a greater good. That is the difference between a rich person and a wealthy person: A rich person has money, but a wealthy person has money with a purpose."

"Wow, I have never thought of it that way before. I just always heard that money is the root of all evil."

"That is a misquoted passage, as you will see in four weeks." Susan had a smile on her face as she started to let the cat out of the bag on her surprise way of teaching Kate the lessons she needed to learn.

"Four weeks? What's in four weeks?"

"In four weeks you will have lunch with a wealthy friend of mine. Kate, I took the liberty of booking lunch for you and me with a few friends over the next five Thursdays. Will that work for you?"

"Uh, sure. I guess. I mean, I would love to. Who are the friends?"

"You will find out who they are each week when we meet with them. They are some very successful and high-profile people who are part of a monthly study group I belong to. We are very diverse, but we have all helped each other learn the lessons you are struggling with. It all stems from understanding the Theology of the Image."

"Okay, great. What am I going to learn?"

"That I will tell you. Today you learned to always judge yourself and your actions by asking yourself whether or not it is a reflection of God's Image. Next week, you will learn about personal growth. The week after that you will learn about ambition. The third week you will learn about goals. In four weeks, as promised, you will learn about wealth. Then, the fifth week you will learn about character. How does that sound?"

"It sounds like the chance of a lifetime."

"Let's hope so. I have big dreams for you!"

"I can't wait!"

"I am afraid you will have to, but it will be great fun when we get there."

The two women spent the rest of their lunch talking about their personal histories, getting to know each other, what they liked to do, and their future dreams. Susan was taking a real liking to this young woman, Kate, and was eager to share the power of a life transformed by the Theology of The Image.

4

Defining Success

"In the end, we strive for human potential not to display the power of humans, but to display the power of God."

As promised, on the next Thursday, Susan and Kate met at a coffee shop in Bellevue and headed north on 405, then west on 520, taking the exit to what is one of the wealthiest neighborhoods in the Seattle area – Hunt's Point. Traveling slowly through the quiet neighborhoods, they finally turned off of the street and came to a large double gate that protected a driveway leading to a beautiful home, though Kate couldn't see it from where they were. Susan pushed the button on the monitor.

"Susan! Welcome. Come right in," said the voice. Slowly the gates began to open and Susan drove through and down the driveway.

"Nice place," Kate said in awe as she began to see the home in all of its grandeur. The home sat on four manicured acres of Lake Washington waterfront with ninety-five hundred square feet of living space and a two thousand square foot boat house. Neatly tucked away from the road, it was a place of quiet solitude for its fast-paced owner.

"So, are you going to let me in on the secret of who we are going to see?" Kate asked. "I know it is about personal development, but who does the house belong to?"

"This is the home of Keith Harris, a good friend of mine."

"Keith Harris the motivational speaker?"

"Exactly the one. You've heard of him?"

"Well, he *is* one of the best known speakers in America. I have read a couple of books by him and heard him speak at a conference once. I didn't know he lived in Bellevue, though."

"Indeed he does," said Susan as she parked the car in front of the home. "He lives right here and we are going to have lunch with him."

"Sounds great. Let's go!" Kate quickly opened the car door, as did Susan, and they started up the walkway. As they began up the steps the front door opened and out stepped Keith Harris, New York Times best-selling author, syndicated columnist, television personality, in-demand motivational speaker, and friend of Susan Hart's.

"Welcome!" he said in his booming voice!

"Good to see you, Keith," Susan said as she greeted him with a hug. "This is a new friend of mine, Kate Miller."

Keith extended his hand and shook Kate's hand vigorously. "So glad to meet you. Welcome to my home."

"Thank you. It is beautiful. I can't wait to hear what you have to say. Susan told me I was going to meet some fantastic people and we have started off right. I have read a few of your books and heard you speak before, and of course, I have seen your television specials."

"Well, we are going to have a great lunch together. I have a somewhat tight schedule but a friend of Susan Hart's is a friend of mine, so I have some time for lunch today. You know, I do about 150 public appearances and speeches a year, and I have to fly out in a few hours for Atlanta, but in the meantime, let's go to my veranda and have some lunch!"

"That sounds great, Keith," Susan said. The three of them passed through the front door and through Keith's great-room and out onto a large veranda exquisitely decorated with expensive outdoor furniture.

"You ladies sit down and enjoy the weather while I go get the lunch. There is some iced tea to cool you off a little." Keith disappeared back into the house to get lunch.

"He sure seems like a nice guy," Kate noted.

"He is, and he is very spiritual. I think you are really going to enjoy what he has to say. He is recognized as one of the world's foremost experts on human potential, and yet what makes him unique is his perspective on human potential."

"I can't wait."

"I have prepped Keith, knowing that he really only has about an hour. I asked him to talk to you about personal development and personal growth. Some people call it 'self-help' and that is where so many Christians disconnect. They think that we are to have nothing to do with 'self,' and so they avoid it. Unfortunately, they then leave everything up to God, including their growth, and God is waiting for them to actively participate." Susan paused, then began again. "Well, I don't want to steal Keith's thunder so we'll leave it to him."

Kate and Susan each poured themselves some tea and looked at the sailboats passing by on Lake Washington. "Do you remember the old Perry Como song, 'The Bluest Skies You've Ever Seen are in Seattle?'" Susan asked.

"Can't say that I do," Kate replied.

"It's true. A few months of the year, you can't beat it here."

Keith returned to the veranda with a tray that carried three large oriental chicken salads. "Here comes the chef. Made them myself – my specialty," he said as he set each one down on the table in its place.

"This looks delicious," Kate praised.

After they paused and Keith said grace, they began to eat.

"So, Kate, Susan says that you are learning – or wanting to learn – about how to be a Christian in the marketplace, and also what is okay and in line with a spiritual life. Is that right?"

"That's right. I struggle with how aggressively to pursue some of the things I feel are in my heart to pursue. One thing that I think you can help me with is the struggle I feel when I pour effort into improving myself. I hear a lot of Christians say that is in conflict with the biblical principle of 'dying to self.' So, you are the expert. "What think ye?" Kate said this last sentence with a smile on her face.

Keith, also smiling and looking at Susan said, "Wow, big expectations of me." He turned back to Kate. "Kate, I think a lot of the subject. Being a Christian is the most important thing in my life, and everything that I do I want to be a reflection of His life. So the fundamental question I think we as Christians have to answer – as it relates to human potential and self improvement – is this, 'Is God for it or against it?' As you mentioned, many Christians say that self-help is not congruent with the Christian life. I would suggest that they have neither read their Bibles well enough, nor have they applied critical thinking to the issue."

"How so?" Kate asked.

"Let's start with the first question: Is God for it? Some Christians would say 'No,' but that begs the following questions: Does God want you to go backwards and become worse in your spiritual life, your financial life, your relational life, etc.?"

"No, I don't think anyone would say that."

"You're right. They wouldn't. So, does God want us to stay stagnant and do our best to live by the status quo? Doing our best to remain average and just like everybody else?"

"I don't think we should do that either," Kate said.

"There you go. Those are the only three options-- get better, stay the same or get worse. Take your pick. The answer is self-evident, Kate. So what we have to do is to redefine what self-improvement and success are. It is obvious that God wants people to be successful – the word is used over forty times in the Bible – we just have to make sure that we define it as God does. That is the key."

"I see," Kate said.

"So, here is my theory. Susan has told you about the idea of being created in the image of God, right?"

"Yes."

"Okay, so we are to be a reflection of God's image. As we know, God is perfect, and we also know that we are not. My understanding is that in order to bring honor and glory to God, I must be conformed more and more into His image. I know that I will never be perfect, but it does not allow me to shy away from the pursuit of being conformed to His likeness, and do you know how you do that?"

"How?"

"Self-improvement."

"But can we improve ourselves? What about being born with a sinful nature, being given to depravity and all of those ideas?"

"Good questions, but fully explainable. You are right; we are born with a sinful nature. One of my favorite quotes is from G.K. Chesterton, who said, 'Original sin is the only philosophy empirically validated by 3500 years of human history.' What we have to understand is the partnership we make with God."

"Partnership?"

"Yes. We know God gives us the power to change, and He does that through His Holy Spirit. He makes everything available to us. But it is up to us to decide whether or not we will take the gifts and resources He makes available to us and then apply them to our lives. He tells us what to do and gives us the power to do it, but He leaves the decision as to whether or not we will, up to us. All of it though, comes down to the biblical admonition to "Be holy, as I am holy."

"But isn't that talking about holiness?" Kate asked.

"Certainly. But is holiness just refraining from doing bad things? That would be such a small way of looking at it, Kate. Holiness is everything we are. That is the way to look at it. It isn't just what we refrain from doing, but what we do, how we do it, and what we become as we do, and that is self-improvement."

"Okay, but doesn't that lead to self-righteousness and pride?"

"Good points, but moot ones."

"Why?"

"Well, they are moot if we are doing things in the right spirit. If I improve myself so I can stand back and say, 'Look at what a great person I am! Aren't I great?' then of course, we have been corrupted by self-righteousness and pride. But what if we improve ourselves and we stand back and say, 'Do you see how great God is? He has given me the power to improve and grow and get better.'? Now that is the spirit in which I talk about self-improvement. It isn't for my glory, but His. In the end, we strive for human potential not to display the power of humans, but to display the power of God."

"Okay, I'm convinced. So how does it work?"

"I believe that we are made up of three parts, all of which are to be submitted to God: Our bodies, our souls, and our spirits. Do you know the difference?"

"Maybe explain the difference between soul and spirit."

"The body is obvious. It is our physical self, and it is important to do our best with it. The Bible says it is the temple of the Holy Spirit, and I think that means we should treat it well. But you asked about the soul and the spirit. The soul is the part you can't touch. It is the mind, the will, and the emotions. It is all that goes on with us that isn't physical."

"So what about the spirit?" Kate asked.

"The spirit is that part of us that is designed to communicate with God. It utilizes the soul and the body to express itself, but it is the spirit that is transformed by God."

"So how does all of that fit with personal development?"

"I like to teach people that by seeing ourselves in these three areas, we have a better understanding about how we can improve ourselves. Let's look at the body; it is fully within our understanding of God to treat our bodies well. We should eat right and exercise. We should refrain from doing things like smoking or excessive drinking or anything else that would put our bodies at risk. In short, we should use our bodies to reflect the image of God."

"What about our souls? How do we improve our souls?"

"We think about it in the different aspects of the soul: The mind, the will, and the emotions. Let's look at each. By giving us our mind, God has given us the most incredible tool imaginable. The average human uses less than ten percent of the mind's capacity. It begs the question: Why did God give us so much capacity? The answer is obvious. He wants us to use it! So we can reflect His image by growing in our intellect. We can come to better understanding of the world around us. We can increase our knowledge, and greater than that, we can increase our wisdom."

"What is the difference between knowledge and wisdom? Aren't they the same?"

"No, not at all. Knowledge is information. Wisdom is the proper understanding and application of knowledge. Lots of people have knowledge, but fewer have the wisdom to apply the knowledge they have in the best way possible for themselves and others. So that is the mind. Then you have the will. The will is like a muscle. It is what we use to apply our knowledge and wisdom. For example, we may have the knowledge that we need to stop smoking. We may even know *how* to stop smoking. But there is just one little problem: We may not have the *will* to stop smoking. We have to train that will to be strong enough to help us do the things we know we should to conform to the image of God. That takes willpower, and of course, our willpower is strengthened by God, but ultimately, we make a choice."

"So how do you strengthen your will?"

"I think it involves two parts. First, prayer. We should always be praying that God gives us what we need to be strengthened inside so we can live as a reflection of His image. Second, we have to train our will."

"Train it?"

"Yep, little by little. Each time we make a decision that represents a small victory of doing what we should be doing over what we would rather be doing, we strengthen the will and make it easier for us to do what is right the next time, but the reverse is also true: Each time we don't use our will, we weaken it so the next time, we may make a bigger mistake."

"All right, I can get that. What about the emotions?"

"Ah, emotions. What a ride they can be – true?"

"I'll say!" Both Susan and Kate laughed at this.

"Emotions are such a gift from God. Yet, they can be tricky. We can be led astray by our emotions. They are designed to help us feel life in all of its greatness as well as it's tragedy. Can we grow emotionally? Absolutely, and we should. If, for instance, someone experiences pain or suffering as a child, they may have some emotional instability as an adult. Does God want that person to grow? Absolutely!"

"So in every area, we should be committed to personal development."

"In every area of life, Kate. Those are just the three areas I start with. But I would contend that what we know from God, we should be committed to becoming the best in every area of our lives."

"To reflect His image and demonstrate His glory to the world," Kate added.

Keith turned to Susan and said, "By golly, she's a quick learner." They all laughed.

They were finishing their lunch by now and Keith looked at his watch. "I would love to stay here and talk some more, but I really need to leave for the airport in about fifteen minutes. You are more than welcome to stay and enjoy the view and let yourselves out if you like."

"No," Susan began, "I need to get back to the office and get some things done myself, so we will get going too." She turned to Kate. "Any last questions or thoughts?"

"No, this has been very helpful, Keith. It helps me understand that personal growth is not only okay with God, but it is in His plan. It reflects His image."

"That it does, Kate, and that is all that matters. Whatever area you can grow in, by all means, do so!"

The three of them arose and headed to the door. "Kate," Keith said, "If I can help you in any other way, you just let me know. A friend of Susan's is a friend of mine, and now of course, you are a friend of mine directly!" He shook their hands and Susan thanked him again as they headed out the door.

As the gates closed behind Susan and Kate and they turned back onto the road that would take them out of Keith Harris' neighborhood, Kate thanked Susan for the opportunity. "Susan, this is so kind of you to do this. I mean, here you just met me on the bus and now you are teaching me these great things and introducing me to these successful people. I just want you to know how much I appreciate it."

"Susan, it is my pleasure. I believe it was a divine appointment. Besides, I am just passing along what someone taught me."

"Well, you sure started me out at the top with lunch with Keith Harris."

"Well, Keith is one of the greatest guys in the world, but I am guessing that come next week, you will be even more enthralled with our class fieldtrip."

"Oh yeah, who is next on the docket?"

"That is a secret. But I will tell you this: She is one of the most powerful women in the world."

"I can't even guess. Who is it, Susan?"

Susan Hart got a sly smile on her face as she said, "You'll see, Kate. You'll see. Just be prepared for a great time."

"Okay. I trust you!"

5

Christians and Ambition

"God is the original big dreamer."

Kate arrived at Susan's office suite exactly on time – 11:30 – the next week. Kate was always prompt. She grew up with parents who were very good people, but who didn't set many goals for themselves. They were loving, decent people who instilled so many great attributes in Kate, attributes that she wanted to use to help her grow even further and use as a platform for a better life. She wanted a life filled with purpose and passion, not just the same old thing. This is why she was so excited to see a new world, a world of endless opportunities. Susan Hart was definitely a Godsend.

As she entered into the suite, Susan's administrative assistant barely looked up as she greeted Kate. Kate felt like she was now a regular. Across the room she could see Susan sitting in the living area along with another woman. They were engaged in what was obviously a lively discussion. Nearby a young man and woman, both dressed for business, were sitting together at another table, also having a discussion. Kate wondered what their connection was.

Kate approached Susan and the other woman, keeping an eye mainly on the other woman so as to see who this mystery woman was – especially considering the lead-in that Susan had given her as "one of the most powerful women in the world." As Kate got to about twenty feet away, she began to recognize the woman. At about ten feet, Susan rose and greeted her just as she figured out who Susan's friend was.

"Hello Kate, welcome." The other woman rose as Susan took Kate's hand in hers. "Kate, I would like to introduce you to one of my lifelong, best friends, Senator Margaret Phillips." Senator Margaret Phillips is the senior Senator from Washington, as well as the ranking member of some of the Senate's most powerful committees. She has for the last two Presidential elections made the short list for Vice-President for her party and is strongly considered a shoe-in for a future cabinet post.

Senator Phillips extended her hand to Kate. "How do you do, Kate? Susan has told me a little about you. I am looking forward to our conversation today."

"Senator Phillips. It is great to meet you, too. I am so surprised. Susan told me I would be meeting someone very special today, but this is even better than I had hoped for. I have followed your career closely. You are such a great example for me."

"Oh thank you, Kate. That is nice of you to say. I look forward to it, too." Senator Phillips motioned toward the younger man and woman seated nearby. That is Mark and Jennifer. They are my assistants. Mark and Jennifer both looked and smiled at Kate.

Susan suggested that the three of them sit back down and talk. Kate sat down and immediately thought about how great the couch felt. This was definitely a better couch than her cheap version in her living room. Everything in Susan's office was top of the line and you could feel it – even in the first seconds of sitting on the couch.

Susan started the conversation. "Kate, Margaret and I have been friends since the fifth grade if you can believe it. We have shared so many things together, but above all else, we share our faith. That is what has been the driving factor for both of us in achieving what we have. We hold each other accountable, challenge and encourage each other, and have remained close friends through thick and thin."

"That sounds beautiful."

"It has been," Senator Phillips agreed.

"I have asked Margaret to talk to you about something she is very passionate – and articulate – about," Susan continued. "I have asked her to share her thoughts on ambition. I know from our discussions that is something you struggle with and it is something Margaret and I have had more than our share of discussions on throughout the years. Early on though, Margaret made a discovery that has been so good for us, because whenever one of us has been considering something, it has helped us decide whether or not we should. Now, I don't want to steal her thunder, so I am going to ask her to do the talking."

Just then one of Susan's staff came from a door on the other side of the office. As it opened, Kate could see that there was a fairly large kitchen on the other side. The staff person was carrying a large serving tray with drinks, silverware and three bowls of soup on it.

"Margaret, I hope you don't mind the casual approach. Otherwise we can go to the dining table."

"No, this is fine. Casual is great." Senator Phillips turned to Kate. "Kate, Susan and I have had much more casual than this. She and I used to sit in our pajamas and eat popcorn, watch movies and call boys on the telephone – that's casual."

"Only when my mom didn't catch us calling the boys," Susan reminded her.

"That's right. On a few occasions, Susan's mom gave us teenagers quite the lecture on decorum. I guess it wasn't okay for us to be calling boys." She and Susan smiled as they remembered their childhood long ago.

"Okay, enough of old home week. Let's get down to business."

Susan thanked the person who had brought them their lunch.

"Kate, I know you said you followed my career, but I thought I would give you an overview nonetheless. Susan and I grew up lower middle class--not a lot of money to splash around. We both came from loving homes, just not terribly ambitious homes."

"That sounds like mine," Kate said.

"I remember wanting so much more out of life. I figured that I could be loving *and ambitious,* so through high school I played three sports and ran for student government. I ended up as the student body president, surprise, surprise. From there I was accepted to a number of superb colleges, but chose Princeton. From Princeton I went to work on Wall Street and after a few years I went back to school at the Wharton School of Business. After Wharton, I came back home to Seattle and began a career with a local firm here that specializes in commercial development. I rose through the ranks there and soon became the first female President in the history of the firm – age thirty-four.

"Now, I had always followed politics, but had never been terribly involved outside of voting, going to the occasional fundraiser, and donating some money, but that all changed when some issues arose that really bothered me. I felt like the people we had elected weren't serving the people as they should. So, given that I had great name recognition because of my high profile in the Seattle area,

I decided to do the impossible: I ran for the United States Senate."

"How did you pull that off, I mean with no background in politics?" Kate asked.

"Kate, timing is everything in life. It just happened that there weren't many other people interested in running against the incumbent because of his high approval ratings. So the field of competition wasn't thick. Secondly, my party wanted to run a strong woman. Lastly, I was willing to spend some of my own money – to the tune of almost a million dollars, which was really big when I ran the first time over a decade ago. Long story short, I won. My opponent made some mistakes, some bad votes, and some comments that rubbed the electorate the wrong way, and the rest, as they say, 'is history.'"

"Wow, that is an incredible story. You must have so much faith in yourself to continue stepping out and trying things like that."

"Faith yes, but not in myself. Well, I certainly know what my strengths are, but ultimately, I have faith in God. When I have faith in God, then it enables me to utilize my strengths and try whatever it is I feel like I should try. It allows me to be as ambitious as I can be."

"Ambition. That's what Susan said you wanted to talk to me about, right?"

"Correct. It is something that many Christians misunderstand."

"How so?" Kate asked.

"Susan has shared with you about being created in the Image of God, right?"

"Yes."

"Good, because that is where it all starts. The first question I had to ask when I struggled with ambition was, 'Is God ambitious?' I had to decide whether or not God was by nature, in His character, ambitious. If He was, then it made ambition within the realm of possibility for me, because I am created in His image."

"That makes sense," Kate said, following along.

"So, is God ambitious, Kate?"

"Uh, I guess so. I mean, I can't imagine Him as some lethargic, cosmic couch potato." The ladies laughed at that.

"No, certainly not. In fact, I believe that God is by nature the most ambitious. Think about it. Before there was anything, God had an idea – an ambitious idea. He decided to create a couple of hundred million *galaxies*." She said *galaxies* for emphasis. "That makes my ambitious plans so many years ago to change the skyline of Seattle pale in comparison. When compared to how ambitious God is, I could be as ambitious as I wanted and it still wasn't even in His league. That gave me a lot of freedom.

"Then He created mankind and told them, starting with just two people, to go and make dominion over the earth. His ambition extended to His creation. His plan was for us to be ambitious as a reflection of His image.

"Soon, things went awry with humanity and again God was ambitious. He sent his Son to earth to take back humanity for himself. Imagine God becoming man in ancient Israel, all with the plan of saving humanity. Ambitious? Absolutely."

"Okay, I can see how God can be – and is – ambitious. But what about us?" Kate asked. "What about the fact that we are supposed to not long for the things of this world, for worldly wealth, etc.? How do you know that the ambition inside is okay? I guess I don't trust myself."

"That is a very good question, Kate. Do you remember earlier when Susan alluded to the fact that I made a discovery in this concept?"

"Yeah."

"You know that Susan and I, and Keith Harris – who you met last week – all belong to a monthly Bible Study, right?"

"Yes."

"It was in that Bible Study, perhaps twenty years ago, that I made a discovery. I was assigned to lead the study that week and I wanted to do it on ambition. All of the people in the study were up and comers, all relatively successful, with more success to come. I was really grappling with this, so I did a New Testament study on the word ambition, and what I found changed my life forever."

"And the lives of those who heard it in that study," Susan added.

"Here is what I found. First, God had an ambitious plan for His followers. He took a rag tag group of fishermen and tax collectors and told them to go start an organization that today has over one billion adherents, outposts on every continent, gives billions of dollars a year to charity, and has built hospitals, schools, and other social organizations in every region on earth. Ambitious, yes?"

"It sure was," Kate agreed.

"His plan was ambitious and He wanted His followers to be ambitious. God is the original big dreamer, but here is the truth that gave me the key to unlocking my potential as it related to ambition."

"What was that?" Kate asked.

"I did a quick study of the word 'ambition' and found that every time it was mentioned in a negative sense, it was always preceded by the same one word. Do you know what that one word was?"

"No, what?'

"It was the word 'selfish.' That blew me away. Every instance it was 'selfish ambition' that God was concerned with. We have taken that to mean ambition was bad. Not so. *Selfish ambition.* That is what God says we are to stay away from."

"That makes sense, but how do you know if you are being selfish or not?"

"That is something for you to decide. Only you can know for sure. There are some things you can do to become clear, but ultimately, only you know your heart. One thing you can do, as I have, is to have a group of trusted counselors around you who will give you honest and open feedback. They need to be people like my Bible Study friends, who will look you straight in the eye and tell you when they think you are off. We all need that feedback from trusted advisors. Of course, the more you pray and study the Bible, the more in tune with God's plan you will be and you will sense it in your spirit whether or not you are being selfish or not."

"So how do you know, I mean personally."

"That is a good question. I will tell you, it can be hard, especially where success is concerned. Money and power are tempting, and corrupting if you aren't careful. Don't get me wrong. Money and power are not bad inherently, but our sinful nature is given to using them in negative ways. That is what we must watch for.

"Let me tell you about when I ran for the Senate. I was well-known around here and the state as well, I guess.

There was nobody stepping up who brought much excitement to the powers that be, and they had heard that I had a bee in my bonnet about a couple of things, so they began recruiting me to run. It was heady stuff. They come around and promise of money and support, all the while telling you how fantastic you are and what a great leader you will be, and that's just the beginning."

"How so?" Kate asked.

"That's just the local powers that be. Then the Senators from your party start calling, and the Governors, and to top it off, if your party holds the Presidency at the time, as mine did, the White House begins the pressure, offering all kinds of support and money. As you can imagine, when the President of the United States calls and encourages you to make the run, it can give you quite a bit of ambition…. Namely, *selfish ambition*.

"That is where you have to be entirely self-aware. I needed to get away by myself and ask why I might be considering this. Truth be told, while the position itself holds some prestige, running for the Senate is terribly difficult and tedious. It is more work than the average person is willing to give, but it is alluring. It is easy to begin to believe what people tell you about yourself – that you are the best thing to happen to the state in a long time. Getting away to be by myself was the best thing I could do."

"Why is that?"

"Because it gave me a chance to deal with that tiny but powerful seven letter word: S-E-L-F-I-S-H. I had to ask myself why I was considering it. Was it for the power? The fame? The lucrative payoff when I was done with a political career? Was it so others would think more of me? What was driving me? That was the question: *What was driving me?*"

"And...?" Kate prodded.

"And when I got alone I realized that I wasn't being driven by those selfish desires. I knew well enough that those things were not of lasting interest to me. I knew they were fading illusions and that people's opinions and wealth can come and go – and do. I came to the conclusion that this was an opportunity for me to do something great – to really make a lasting difference in the world around me. I knew that even though I had no political experience whatsoever, that God was calling me to do the ambitious thing: To announce my candidacy for the United States Senate. I decided I would go for it and have no other option than winning. I decided that I would be myself and let the voters decide whether or not they wanted me, and they did!"

"So, how is it now? How does this play out for you now that you have achieved it all?"

"Oh, Kate, it is more at the forefront of my mind now more than ever. I consider and confront naked selfish ambition every day of my life. Remember, the U.S. Senate is called 'The Most Exclusive Club in the World.' It is home to one hundred highly successful men and women, and of the one hundred, I would say eighty-five of them are completely driven by their own ambition. I work every day with ninety-nine strong and capable men and women who run the most powerful nation on earth, with trillions of dollars at their disposal, and virtually every one of them is asking themselves how everything they do can best serve one person: *Them.* So, I make sure every day I go to the hill that I run everything through one idea, which is, 'How can I be a servant today?'"

"A servant?"

"Yes, a servant. If my goal is to help others and to serve others, then I can undertake the most ambitious plans I can because I know that it is not for my own gain, but for the betterment of others, and ultimately, for the glory of God. That is why I do what I do. Yes, there are more than enough temptations for me to want to serve myself, and I battle those vigilantly. I try my best to keep my eye on the ball and be as ambitious as I can for the good of others and to be the reflection of His image. When you do that, you will do well."

The three ladies had finished their soup while talking and Mark and Jennifer were making their way over to Senator Phillips. "I see that I am being ushered away to my next appointment," Senator Phillips said, beginning to stand. Mark handed her a business card and she handed it to Kate. "Kate, I know we didn't get much time together today – I don't get much time with anybody really – but please know that if I can ever do anything for you, I certainly will."

"Thank you so much, Senator Phillips. I appreciate the time you have taken. It really makes sense to me. I can begin thinking about my ambition and whether or not it is selfish. That is a fantastic point of reference."

Senator Phillips reached out and gave Kate a hug good-bye. As she pulled her close, Senator Phillips whispered in Kate's ear: *Always be ambitious, Kate.* Senator Phillips then gave her old friend Susan a hug good-bye as well and was gone in moments, taken away by her aides.

Susan and Kate sat back down on the couch. "Amazing woman, huh?" Susan asked.

"I'll say. She is something else."

"So what did you think?"

"It all makes sense. It isn't about ambition. It is about selfish ambition. Just like you and Senator Phillips have figured out, I just have to begin asking myself the same thing: Is what I am contemplating ambitious or is it selfishly ambitious."

"And Kate, do you know what I have found?"

"What's that?"

"I have found that so many people are selfishly ambitious so they can achieve certain status or material wealth, but if I keep myself from that, and am solely ambitious for His glory, everything that I need and want comes with it. The Bible says to, 'Seek first the Kingdom of God, and His righteousness, and all these things shall be added to you.' When I keep my eye on doing His will – as ambitious as that is – He keeps me and my needs in mind. Just look around. I am in want for nothing. God takes care of me."

"It sure looks like He does," Kate said with a smile.

"Now, for next week."

"Yes, next week. How can you top this week?"

"I don't know that I can top it, but you will be happy I am sure. Next week I am going to introduce you to someone who is younger than you. Yet he is very rich, famous, handsome and a nation-wide celebrity."

"More important than that – is he single?" Kate said laughing. Susan laughed out loud as well.

"As a matter of fact, he is. But, keep your mind on the matters at hand, young lady," Susan said, feigning a scold. You can learn some very good lessons from this young man. He has his head squarely on his shoulders and has been in our Bible Study for three years now."

"And his name is…" Kate prodded.

"Don't get ahead of yourself, young lady. Soon enough you will know. I like to keep you in suspense. It assures me that you will show up next week."

"I don't know. Meeting a good-looking, famous, rich and single celebrity… I may have other things to do next week."

"Uh-huh. I'll see you at 11:30."

"That you will, Susan."

Kate left Susan's office that day with a new take on ambition. Now she knew she could be as ambitious as her heart would allow her to be – as long as it wasn't selfish ambition, but ambition that reflected the image of God.

6

God and Goals

"Hold all of your goals and dreams loosely."

The next Thursday, Susan and Kate left Susan's office at 11:40 and drove north to Kirkland. Once there, Susan navigated their way to the training facility of Seattle's NFL football team. As they pulled into a parking spot Kate said, "Oh, a football player. Which one?"

"Observant, aren't you?" Susan said dryly. "Today you are going to meet a young man that I think very highly of. As soon as he got here to Seattle three years ago, the first thing he did was seek out a group of mentors to help him in life, not just football. That is how he ended up in our Bible Study. His name is Cory Thompson."

"The quarterback?!"

"Yes, the quarterback. You follow football?"

"I sure do, and he is one of my favorites."

"Great. That will make it even more fun. Cory is one of the best quarterbacks in the NFL. He led the league in touchdown passes last year. He was a Rose Bowl Champion twice and won the Heisman Trophy his senior year. According to the papers, he makes $4,000,000 a year, but above and beyond all of his accomplishments, he is one of the finest young men I have ever met. He is thoughtful, kind and a true gentleman.

"Well, what are we waiting for?" Kate asked.

"Let's go!"

As they entered the facility, they stopped at the front desk and signed in. They were then given an escort to the field where the team was just finishing up. There they watched the team's final minutes of practice before they broke for lunch. At noon sharp they broke and Cory jogged over to Susan and Kate, taking his helmet off as he did. "Hello, Mrs. Hart," he said.

"Cory, for the one hundredth time, call me Susan!" She turned to Kate. I have told him this before. He is just too much of a gentleman. Turning back to Cory, she said, "Cory, meet my friend Kate Miller. Kate, meet Cory Thompson."

"I'd shake your hand," Cory said, "but it's all sweaty. Hope you don't mind."

"Oh no, I understand. Nice to meet you."

"I asked the trainer to save us a small conference room, if you like."

"Sounds great," Susan said. "Lead the way."

Once back in the building they went into a small conference room that sat about eight people. Once they were seated, Susan began. "Cory, I wanted to get together with you and Kate because you have so much in common." Kate wondered to herself what those things could possibly be. "You are both young, have tremendous gifts and talents, and a great deal of potential." Cory smiled at Kate. "And you are both Christians, so that is the best thing to have in common."

"It sounds like you are quite an impressive person, Kate." Cory said.

"So Cory," Susan continued, "I know your break is short, but I wanted to have you meet Kate and see if you could give her some insights that you have gained as it relates to your faith, particularly in the area of achievement and goal-setting."

"Sure. I would be happy to. I don't know how much I can help, but I have a few ideas that help me. I am no biblical scholar, and I am still learning myself, but I have figured a few things out. What exactly can I help you with, Kate?"

"Okay, here is one. Goals. Every time I go to a workshop or listen to a speaker who talks about success and business, I hear that goal-setting is the key to high achievement. Yet whenever I hear a sermon, it seems like if you plan too far out in the future, you are being presumptuous. At the seminar, I hear that I should set ten year goals, five year goals, and one year goals, and then at church I hear that I may not even be here tomorrow and should take only one day at a time."

"Okay. Any specific Bible passages you are thinking about?"

"Yeah, actually. One from James. The one that says we shouldn't say that we are going to do this or that but that we should say only if the Lord wills it. Do you know which one I am talking about?"

"I do. James 4:14-15. That is the one most people use to say that you shouldn't set goals. I have a different take on it, though--one that utilizes the power of goal-setting while fully understanding and submitting to the sovereign plan of God."

"Okay, hit me with it."

"Glad to. You see, I started goal setting when I was in the fifth grade. I wanted to play on the junior high team when I was in the sixth grade. We had sixth through eighth for junior high. I wanted it so bad that I threw passes every day all year round. I went to numerous camps each summer. My goal drove me to excel, and I got it. I was the starting quarterback for three years. Then my goal was to start on the high school varsity as a freshman. It drove me to reach even deeper. Then, a bump in the road. A week before my freshman year of football started, I fell out of a tree and broke my arm. I was out for eight weeks. By the time I was ready, there were only a couple of weeks left and the coach wanted to let the senior quarterback play the season out. That was the first conflict between my goals and God's plan. That time off from football was what I needed to get adjusted to high school, to let the other kids get to know me, and for me to learn to improve my study habits. In hindsight, it was just what I needed. It didn't fit my goal, but it was God's plan and the first time I had to learn to accept that over my goals.

"I spent the next three years as the starter and ended up second all time in our state for passing touchdowns. I was given a full ride scholarship to UCLA and ended up winning the Rose Bowl twice and the Heisman my senior year."

"Sounds like you passed the bumps in the road," Kate said.

"Not quite. When the draft came, I was the fourth quarterback taken, still first round but fourth in my own position. My goal was top three picks, and certainly first at QB. Needless to say, I was disappointed."

"So what happened?"

"People thought I was too small. One team even asked if I would switch to wide-receiver if they drafted me. Seattle finally drafted me and gave me a shot. My goal was to be second string since we had a great starter and a nine year veteran who played backup the year before. By the first game, I had been put at second on the depth chart, so I achieved my goal. After the fourth game of my rookie year, our starter broke his leg in a motorcycle accident and there I was: The 'too small' quarterback was now starting in the NFL. I set my next goal to win seven of the twelve remaining games. We won eight and finished ten and six. Then, I hit my stride and came back to start from then on."

"So what lessons have you learned, Cory?" Susan asked.

"A few. First, set goals. Dream big. God gives us dreams in our hearts and we should follow them. If we obey and love Him, he gives us the desires of our hearts. Second, hold all of your goals and dreams loosely."

"Loosely? What do you mean?" Kate asked.

"I call them faith goals, or prayer goals. You see, I set the goal for what I want to achieve – what I believe God wants me to achieve based on the gifts, talents and desires He has given me. Then I hold them in my hands with palms up. They just rest there. If God wants to take them out, He can. He can replace them with something smaller or, many times, He replaces them with something bigger. That has been my experience anyway. That solves the problem of presumption because while you are setting goals and dreaming of what your life can become, you are still allowing God to control your life and determine the outcome."

"That sounds like it takes care of both sides."

"It does. It may be simple, but that is how I see it. One thing is, it is hard when God takes something out of our hands. That is really where the rubber hits the road. That is the test as to whether or not you truly trust God with your goals. It is easier to praise Him when you get your goals than to thank Him when you don't. But thanking Him when you don't will build more character."

The door opened and a young man leaned in and said, "Ten minutes, Cory."

"Okay thanks, Pete." The door shut as Pete left. "I don't know if that helps, but I really do think that God wants us to have big goals. Why else would He give us our minds to set them and plan them, and our hearts to dream them and be passionate about them? I think it is fully within the realm of Christianity to be a high achiever and successful."

"That's really good stuff, Cory."

"Oh, and one more thing. Our goals are always to be for His glory and for His gain. Another verse I keep in mind is from Second Corinthians 5:9, which says that we make it our goal to please Him. I'm not much for wearing my faith on my shirtsleeve, but I do use everything that God has given me for His glory and His gain. Yes, I get to enjoy a life that includes a lot of money, but when asked, I give Him the glory for what I have become, and I use the fruit of my skills and success to help others. I am a very aggressive giver of my money. In fact, I have more charitable goals than I do anything else. It all comes back to serving God and reflecting His image, as Susan likes to say." Susan smiled. "See, I'm listening in those Bible studies, Susan." Now Cory had a big grin on his face.

"I always knew you were."

"Listen, I still have to get a quick bite of a protein bar and some water or something, so I need to get out of here. I wish we had more time."

"That's okay, we appreciate the time you gave us. Thanks, Cory."

They all stood. "You are very welcome. Kate, I hope to see you again soon."

"You too, Cory. Thank you."

As they left the conference room, Cory turned left to the locker room and Susan and Kate turned back to the front reception area.

"Nice guy, huh?" Susan asked as the crossed the parking lot to the car.

"Very nice. Smart, too."

"Yes, very smart."

"And cute."

Susan gave Kate the *I can't believe you said that* smirk.

"I'll give you that, Kate--he's cute."

"And single."

"Okay, okay," said Susan, smiling.

Susan pressed the remote and they heard the familiar chirp of locks opening.

"Get in the car, Kate," Susan deadpanned.

As they pulled into the parking garage so Kate could get her car and go home, Susan prepped for the next meeting. "Kate, have you ever met a billionaire?"

Kate didn't have to think long. "I don't think so."

"Well, get set because you will next week."

Kate got excited. "Really? Who?" Then she realized Susan would not tell her.

"Can't tell you. Don't want to ruin the surprise. You'll find out next week."

"Okay. Before I leave, will you help me reach a new goal?"

"Sure, what is it?"

"My newest goal is to get you to set up a date with me and Cory."

Susan rolled her eyes jokingly. "I'll see what I can do. I should have never encouraged you to dream big."

"That's me. I'll see you next week." With that, Kate was out the door and off to her own car, thinking now about all of her dreams and goals.

7

Wealth – A Matter of the Heart

"Do You Love God or Money?"

Susan had a special day planned for Kate so she asked her to be at Hart's headquarters around 10:30 so they could drive south down to Boeing Field. As they drove, Susan addressed a topic from the week before. "Kate, I'm afraid I can't do what I said I would do for you."

"What's that?"

"I can't call Cory for you."

Kate turned to Susan. "Why?"

Susan smiled. "Because he already called me to see if you might be interested in getting together sometime."

"What did you tell him?" Kate said excitedly.

"I played it cool for you. I said I would check."

"You're so smooth! I love that."

"So I can give him your number?"

"Absolutely!"

"Okay then, I will."

Susan exited off of I-5 South and circled down and around to the east side of Boeing Field where many of the wealthiest Seattleites keep their aircraft in inconspicuous hangers. Kate still had no idea what they were doing, and she had no idea that these hangers even existed or who used them.

Susan pulled the car into a parking lot next to one of the larger hangers. On the single, drab gray door, there was a sign that said simply, "Mitchell Industries."

Susan announced their arrival. "This is it – the hanger where one of the richest men in the world keeps his airplanes, or at least a few of them, and a few helicopters."

Kate looked at the door. "Mitchell Industries. Andrew Mitchell, the Cell Phone King?"

"The one and only. Andrew is another old friend of mine. Forbes lists him as in the top forty richest Americans. He has been worth billions for at least ten years now. He made his money in cell phones – thus the nick name – but as most extremely wealthy people do, he diversified. He is now in software, biotech, and of course, real estate, and, he *loves* his aircraft, as you will see soon."

"Okay, I am ready. And Susan?"

"Yes?"

"Thank you so much for this. I know that this is a once in a lifetime chance and I appreciate it more than you can ever imagine."

"It is my pleasure, Kate. You have tremendous potential. I see something special in you and I want to help you in any way I can."

They got out of the car and went to the door. There they pressed a button on a speaker and waited. "May I help you?" the voice asked.

"Susan Hart to see Andrew Mitchell."

"Okay, come down the hall to the right and up the stairs. At the top press the button next to the door."

The door buzzed and Susan and Kate walked through and up to the next door. There they were again buzzed through. Once they entered the doorway they came to a reception area with a few couches. Just off the reception area was a security room with a bank of televisions monitoring the property. A woman came in and welcomed them. She then asked them to follow her to Andrew's office.

She led them down a short hall, and into an office. There sat Andrew Mitchell, talking on the telephone. He finished shortly and was up and around the edge of the desk in no time. He hugged Susan and kissed her on the cheek.

"Andrew, I want you to meet the friend I told you about, Kate Miller."

He extended his hand. "Very nice to meet you, young lady. If you are half as lovely as Susan says you are, we will get along terrifically."

"Thank you very much. It is so nice to meet you, Mr. Mitchell."

"Please, call me Andrew – Not Andy! – but Andrew." He said this with a smile as he always thought Andy too boyish for a billionaire.

"Do you like airplanes, Kate?" Andrew asked.

"I sure do. Not the airports or long flights, but I like airplanes." They all nodded knowingly.

"Well, today you will get a look at some very special airplanes. Let's go look downstairs."

When they got downstairs they opened the door into the hanger. It was an extremely large room with no dividers, just like you would expect an airplane hanger to look. The floor was bright white and glossy. It looked clean enough to eat off of.

Across the hanger sat numerous aircraft. As they walked by the first one Andrew began the descriptions. "This is a Cessna Caravan. It has wheels and floats so I can do either water or land. I use this mainly to go to my summer place in the San Juans. It is like the minivan of airplanes.

"These next two are Falcons. I don't use them much. They get used by executives in my companies. Also, we donate it to charity sometimes, and we lend them to some medical missions that need emergency transportation. That is a great use for them."

"It sounds like it," Kate said.

"We have another one, but it is gone today."

They came to another, larger jet. "This is my Challenger. A beautiful jet."

At the end of the row they came to a jet with stairs up to it. This is the Rolls Royce. This is the Gulfstream 550. If you are going to travel, *This is the way to do it!* Care to take a look?"

"Oh, I would love to."

The three of them went up and took a look around the finest corporate jet made. Nothing but beauty on the inside--plush leather chairs, a small galley, and polished teak everywhere. There were phones at each sitting area and computers at two of them.

"I can do everything I need here. It isn't Air Force One, but it does the trick. It can go six thousand nautical miles and can fly at a maximum of fifty-one thousand feet."

"It is beautiful," Kate exclaimed.

"Now for another treat. Let's exit the airplane and head back over toward the back side of the hanger and we will go outside."

As they exited the hanger through a door, they came back into the Seattle summer sunshine. Just about seventy-five feet away sat a helicopter. "This is one of my three helicopters. They are Eurocopter Super Pumas – incredible machines. They are beautiful and fun to ride in. Would you like a tour of Mt. Rainier?" They all looked south and saw Mt. Rainier, Washington's highest peak at just over 14,000 feet, sitting there, beckoning them.

"Would I? I would love to!"

"Then let's fire it up." They all got into the helicopter and the pilot soon had them checked in with flight control and airborne. "There are some boxed lunches here, so just eat whenever you like. Should be pretty good. My chef makes a great ham and cheese sandwich." Each of them was wearing a headset so they could hear and talk with each other. The helicopter was configured so they could face each other.

"So, Kate, Susan filled me in a bit, but she said that you are doing some study – and some great field trips it sounds like – so you can find out more about being a Christian and being successful. I'm guessing I am the lesson on money!" Andrew had a great sense of humor and didn't take himself too seriously. He enjoyed meeting all kinds of people and was, in spite of his billionaire style toys, completely lacking in pretension.

"Yes Andrew, you are the 'money lesson' as you put it," Susan said. "I couldn't think of a better person to teach Kate these important lessons, not only from the Bible, but from experience. I know how much you have grappled with your situation as you came into more and more wealth. I thought you could help her understand a few things."

"I would be glad to. Kate, fire away!"

"Okay, let's start with the obvious. The Bible says that money is the root of all evil."

"Good place to start. In fact, that may be the most misquoted – in a well-meaning way – passage in the entire Bible. What it actually says is this: 'The *love of money* is the root of all kinds of evil.' That puts a new meaning to it, doesn't it?"

"It sure does. So how do you take that?"

"Here is my theory. Money is an inanimate object. It is a piece of paper with numbers on it. It is a tool to get things done. It is neither bad nor good. The human heart is bad or good and when a bad heart gets a hold of money, it does bad things. When a good heart gets a hold of money, it does good things. So, for example, I do not love money. I love God, and I love what good my money can be used for. The key is to always be looking at your own heart."

"How so?"

"Well, think of it this way. The money, or the amount of money you have, is really a moot point. We tend to bash rich people, but poor people have their own heart problems. A poor person can be completely content, or they can be filled with greed, envy and bitterness about not having money. A rich person can be humbly filled with gratitude for their good fortune or they can be filled with pride and arrogance. In both the poor person and the rich person, money is beside the point. The real issue is the heart. Ultimately the question is, 'Do you love God or money?'

"You know, our Bible Study group sort of centers around the idea that we were made in the image of God. So I ask myself, 'Does God have a problem with wealth?' Nope. He is wealthy. Many of the main characters in the Bible were wealthy. Now, let me give a caveat here. I am not in any way saying that if you are a Christian, God will make you wealthy or that wealth is a sign of being a spiritual person. If you believe that, you are probably watching the wrong TV preachers! But I am saying that it is completely congruent with the nature of God for people of faith to have wealth, and to use it according to His plan."

"Okay, I buy that. It makes sense. But what about the verse that says that we shouldn't store up for ourselves treasures on earth, but rather to store up treasures in heaven? How do you deal with that and also having so much money and a hanger full of airplanes, if I may be so bold?"

"You may be so bold! I love it. We Christians don't talk enough about this topic. It is one of the most pressing issues of our time, especially for Christians in the western world who have so much. We have to grapple with those passages and come up with reasonable and balanced conclusions."

"So what conclusions have you come to?" Kate asked.

"First of all, again, I know that many men of faith in the Bible were men of means. Second I know that there is a continuum of wealth from having nothing to being the richest person in the world, and everyone falls on that line somewhere. I happen to be near the top, maybe the top 150 in the world, but if you take the *average* American, they are still some of the wealthiest people on earth. So, even if you are poor in America, you are rich by the world's standards. So does that make the poor in America bad, because they are wealthier than others in the third world? I don't think so. What I really think drives these discussions is jealousy and class warfare. The problem is that when you get right down to it, you can't judge a person by what they have or don't have. If you do, there will always be someone who is 'more spiritual' than you because they are poorer, or 'less spiritual' than you because they are richer. In fact, that is a treadmill that is hard to get off of."

"So how do you give it proper perspective?"

"I think each and every conscientious Christian has to go to God personally and to reflect on the condition of their own heart as to whether or not they are focused on the earthly treasures or the heavenly treasures. I can't judge what another person has or doesn't have, because I don't know what they do with their wealth. Let me give you an example. A few folks over the years have given me a hard time for owning beautiful homes – about forty million dollars worth – and over a hundred million dollars worth of airplanes. On the first take, that probably looks gluttonous. But what they don't see is that over the past ten years I have given away over one billion – that's with a 'b' – dollars to charity all over the world. I have personally paid for 100 bed hospitals in some African countries and at least twenty schools in South America that have nearly two thousand students in them."

"But how does that relate to me and the average American?"

"That is my point. It is easy to point the finger at the wealthy, but when you compare percentages and the like, chances are, I am just as charitable, if not more so, than the average American. That isn't to say I am better. I'm not. I just think that we are all in different spots and we all have to encourage each other, no matter how much money we have, to be stewards of the money God has given us."

"Stewards? What do you mean?"

"That's another good point. You see, I don't even consider this money as mine. I truly don't. I hold all of my money in an open hand. I consider every request for help because I don't own the money – God does. So my biggest challenge is to decide what God wants me to do with His money at any given time. Does He want me to buy another company? Does He want me to make my plane available to a group that helps organ donors? Does He want me to help a hospital be built, and if so, do I pay the whole thing or just a part? Believe me, when you achieve more wealth as a Christian, it can make things difficult if you give it the proper thoughtfulness that it deserves. All of a sudden it isn't your money, but God's, and that brings with it a lot of responsibility – and the joy from knowing you are involved in something good."

Andrew turned to the window as they were approaching Mt. Rainer. "Amazing, isn't it? I love to make this trip. I have adopted a local high school down in a poorer section of town, and I bring the business students up here for this trip. There are about thirty of them, so we do it on two different weekends, and we get all three helicopters out and make trips down until they have all seen it. Boy, they love it, and I never get tired of seeing this gorgeous mountain!"

"It sure is beautiful," Susan added.

They took their time flying around the western side of the mountain and then around the south and headed back north along the eastern side before heading back toward Seattle.

As they made their way back, Andrew still had more to share. "You know, Kate, this is a passion of mine. So many Christians have a warped view of wealth. It is a weird topic because so many people feel awkward talking about money. We need to get over that and bring the conversation into the light. We can't shy away from it. We have to get over our judgmentalism and challenge and encourage each other to do the best we can, regardless of our station in life."

"Well, you have certainly given me lots to think about."

"Oh there is more!"

"There is always more with Andrew," Susan jokingly chimed in.

"I am not without my opinions," Andrew said. There are a couple of other thoughts that have been helpful for me to consider. There is a passage in Ecclesiastes that says 'whoever loves money, never has money enough.' That always keeps me in a place where I am monitoring where my heart is, because I know that if I get to where money has a place in my heart, it is an endless void. Once you love money, you can't get enough of it. A friend told me a story of one of America's early wealthy industrialists. He was one of the richest Americans ever, especially if you convert his money to today's dollars. As the story goes, someone once asked him how much money was enough money. His answer? 'Just a little bit more.' Wow. That has always stuck with me."

"Yeah, that is a great story."

"One last thought. In Romans, there is a short list of spiritual gifts. One of the gifts is giving to the needs of others. Now, doesn't that make you wonder how a person could have a life long gift of giving unless they had a life long source of resources? So, that is how I view myself. I have been given the gift of giving and being a steward of resources I am given. But that isn't just for the wealthy. It is for everyone. Even those who live in a hut will from time to time be asked to give generously to someone in need. It all comes back to the heart, Kate. The money is beside the point and when we get caught up on the amounts, we miss the really important question: What is the condition of my heart as it relates to my money and possessions."

"So the focus is less on money and more on keeping my heart right?"

"Exactly. So I go for it, trust God to give me any increase that He wants to give me, and it is my job to watch my heart and utilize that wealth in the way He wants me to. It removes the questions of whether God is for or against wealth, or whether an amount is too big or too little. I feel that it keeps me with my heart in the right place, and at the end of my life, the number in my bank account doesn't matter. My heart does."

"That makes so much sense. I am so glad someone like you has figured it out so it makes it easy for people like me!"

"I am happy to do it, Kate. Well now, what do you say about eating these lunches?"

"Sounds great to me," Susan said. She then grabbed the three boxes and handed one each to Andrew and Kate.

As they flew back to Boeing Field, Andrew told tales of all of the things he had his hands in. Later Susan told Kate that a guy like Andrew doesn't come along very often, and he lives his life at a very high level. Kate and even Susan were amazed at how much he gets done in a day. When they were finished with lunch they had about five minutes left to fly. After clearing approach, the pilot softly landed the Eurocopter. As the blades began to slow to a stop, the three of them got out and began walking back to the hanger. Once inside, Andrew walked the ladies to the door leading to the parking lot.

"Susan, as always, it is good to see you. We are still on for the study next week?"

"Yes, we are. You'll be in town?"

"I will., and I am looking forward to it. Everybody else will be there?"

"As far as I know, they will be."

"Great, and Kate, it was so much fun to meet you. I hope that some of the things I have talked about can help you in some way."

"I already know that it will, Andrew. Thank you so much for the wisdom – and for the ride! That was amazing!"

"My pleasure. Well, I will let you ladies get on your way. I have a few things to do here and then I have to get back to my real office downtown."

"Thanks again, Andrew."

Susan and Kate talked as they drove through the traffic on I-5 North. Susan also shared how she had come to some of the same conclusions as Andrew had. Susan certainly didn't have Andrew Mitchell money, but she was worth well north of a hundred million dollars, so she had learned a thing or two about integrating her financial life with her spiritual life.

Focusing toward next week, Susan hinted at who they would meet for their last meeting. "Next week you will meet a man who has a great deal of influence. He isn't particularly wealthy, but he has been quite successful in his own right. More than anything, he has influence with people who are society's influencers."

"Okay, I can't wait. I am at the point where I trust you completely."

"So, tell me Kate, what are your plans for the future? Have you figured that out yet? I mean, we are almost at the end of our meetings."

"Oh, I am going to look to do something similar to what I was doing. I am thinking about opening my own business. I am just looking for clarity now."

"Well, it will come--in due time."

"Yes, that's what I figure."

When they arrived, Susan and Kate agreed to catch up by phone the following week and set up the exact time for their next meeting. "I have to go to New York for the weekend, so I will call you Tuesday and give you the specifics, okay?"

"That works for me," Kate said.

8

Character and Integrity

"You can serve God and have money, but you cannot serve God and serve money at the same time."

At 11:30 sharp, one week from their previous meeting, Kate arrived for her last meeting with Susan and her friends. Kate didn't know whether or not Susan would keep meeting with her after these lunch engagements were over. That was, after all, the premise for all of their weekly meetings. She hoped that they would stay in touch and develop their friendship, but she also knew how busy a woman like Susan Hart was and that she was already giving so much of her time just to make these meetings happen.

Susan met her up front just as she got off of the elevator and said, "Let's get back on. We have to walk about ten blocks for our meeting this morning and I told him we would be there at 11:45, so we have to go."

"Okay, I am glad I wore shoes I can walk in."

As they walked they chatted about the previous week, particularly about one bit of information Kate wanted to share. "Guess who called me this weekend?"

"Hmm. The President?"

"No, you know. Cory called me on Saturday."

"Really? What did he want?" Susan was playing coy.

"Well, he took me to dinner Monday night. That's a good start."

"Really? How did you like Wild Ginger?"

Kate stopped in her tracks and with mock horror asked, "How did you know? Are you stalking me?"

"No, but a little bird did call me on Tuesday, very excited about a dinner he had the night before. I am a little like his adopted mother, you know."

"Yes, it was very nice. He is so great."

"I think so, too. I am happy for you, Kate."

They continued walking until they had walked the ten blocks north and they stood in front of a large church. Susan said, "We're here."

"A church? We are meeting him here?"

"Yes, that is where you would expect to meet Bill Farmer."

"Bill Farmer. Sounds familiar. Who is he?"

"Bill is the senior pastor here. His congregation is the largest in Seattle and one of the largest in the state. About 4500 people come here every Sunday morning to hear his sermons. What is astounding is that it is a church in the city. Most congregations this size are in the suburbs. To build a congregation like this in the city is really extraordinary."

"Huh, interesting. I have never gone to a big church. I have always gone to smaller churches, maybe three hundred people max."

"Well, I think you are really going to enjoy our meeting. I have nothing but the utmost respect for Bill. He is the one who put together our study that we do. He specifically targeted successful people, or people on the way up, so that he could influence people on a large level. Not many people are comfortable working with high achievers in the church because of all of the issues that we have already covered. You know, a guy like Andrew Mitchell for example. Many pastors would love to have him in their church for the money he may give, but a lot of pastors would feel intimidated by him and find it hard to shepherd a guy like that. People like Andrew and Cory and Keith and Senator Phillips are just people, people like you and me. They need someone to love and care for them just like we do. They need someone to challenge them and encourage them, as well. It takes a special person with special gifts to be able to pull it off. Bill Farmer is one who can do it, and he does it well."

"Well, let's go meet him," Kate said.

"Let's do."

As they entered, Susan recognized the receptionist. "Hello Connie. How are you?"

"I am doing well, Susan. Very well. How are you?"

"I am doing great. We are here to see Pastor Bill."

"I will walk you back to his office. I know he is expecting you."

When they arrived at Bill Farmer's office, it was exactly what Kate would expect a pastor's office to look like. It was carpeted in a deep rich carpet. It had a big desk with a computer on it, and it had bookshelves from the floor to the ceiling, covering almost the entire wall space. In the background there was a soft strain of music to provide the pastoral ambiance. It was very comfortable.

"Hello Susan."

"Hello Bill. This is my friend, Kate."

"Nice to meet you, Kate." He motioned to the couches. "Please sit down."

When they were seated, Pastor Farmer asked Susan how they had met.

"We bumped into each other on the bus and got to talking about things of faith and business, and now I have been dragging her around the city for the last four or five weeks introducing her to some of our friends from our Bible Study Group."

"Oh yeah? Who have you met, Kate?"

"Let's see. Keith Harris, Senator Phillips, Cory Hart, and last week was Andrew Mitchell."

"Wow, so what do you need to talk to me about? I don't know that I can compete with that crew." He chuckled as he said it.

"Oh, Bill, you more than hold your own. I thought that it would be really good for you to talk with Kate about some of the issues of character that go with being a successful person in the marketplace."

"Okay, I would be glad to. But what did the others talk about with you?"

"Well, Keith talked about personal development. Senator Phillips talked about ambition. Cory talked about goals, and Andrew talked about wealth."

"That sounds very interesting, and you learned from people who have lived every principle that they talk about. Nothing better than that."

"So, Bill, what can you share with Kate that will be good for her to hear as it relates to being a Christian, being in the marketplace, being successful and the like?"

"I have given a lot of thought to that question over the years, and like a pastor would, I have five points." Susan and Kate laughed.

"Sounds like a preacher," Susan said.

"So, if you will humor me, I'll share them with you."

"I would love to hear them," Kate said.

"Okay, the first one is obvious but needs to be said. Keep God first. If you can say honestly that God is first in your life, then you are in a good spot. You know, the Bible says that you cannot serve both God and money. The fact is that you cannot serve God and anything else. Money was just the illustration there, probably because God knows that money is the most powerful draw here on earth. You can serve God and *have* money, but you cannot serve God and *serve* money at the same time. It is one or the other. The idea is that you can only serve one master.

"And by serve, the Bible means that they are your master. Obviously, we serve others and are called to. It means that you cannot be mastered by anything else. You cannot be mastered by your career, by your reputation, by money or possessions – nothing should come before your relationship with the Lord.

"There is a Bible verse that says many, in wanting to get rich, have shipwrecked their faith. Most people think that means money is bad. Not so. It simply means that in their pursuit of money, they lost sight of the real prize – a relationship with God. They took God from His place in their lives and replaced it with money. That is the point of that passage. So, number one, Keep God first."

"Got it," Kate said.

"Good." Bill smiled at Susan. "So number two is about character. There is nothing more important to God than the forging of our character. He wants nothing more than for us to be conformed to His image and that means we learn to be like Him in our character. If you think about how to describe the character traits of God, how would you describe Him, Kate?"

"Honest. Fair. Loving." She tipped her head and thought before continuing. "Kind. Patient. Faithful. Integrity."

"Yes, those all describe God, and of course we could go on for some time. God is so deep and rich in who He is. But you make the point. We all know by the very definition of the term 'God' that He represents certain values and character traits, and as Christians, our second priority is to become like Him. We are to seek out His character and then to allow ourselves to be transformed into the same character. That answer is simple. It is hard to do, but simple to say. Our job is to become kind, patient, loving, and filled with integrity – all of the character traits you listed and the rest as well. Character and integrity form the foundation of a successful life."

"So what do you do if you fail, if you do something wrong and your character is shot or called into question?"

"Kate, I don't believe that a sin makes you a person with no character. *Everybody* sins. Everyone does wrong. That is a fact. I believe that integrity is doing the right things and living a godly life, but I also believe that a person maintains their integrity when they do wrong – which we all do – by quickly admitting it and rectifying it."

"Hmm." Kate pondered that one.

"Let me give you an example. Let's talk about the integrity of a structure--maybe a skyscraper, of which we have many here in Seattle. All buildings have stress in their structures and over time they weather and breakdown. Eventually the integrity of a building can be compromised by the little cracks that develop. Now a little crack can't bring a building down, but a big crack can, and do you know what little cracks become if they are left alone – big cracks. That is a great analogy for our own integrity. It is great if there are no cracks, but that is unrealistic. The key is when we develop small cracks to make sure they do not become big cracks. We restore our integrity on a day-to-day basis."

"That makes sense."

"I would like to think so," Pastor Farmer said. "Okay, ready for number three?"

"I am."

"Okay, number three. That has to do with self-discipline. Many Christians don't like anything that uses the word 'self.'"

"Yeah, Keith talked about that a little bit."

"Well, we are called to work on ourselves. It is a 'joint-venture' as many of my business friends like to say. God works on and in us, but we also play a role in that. We are called to exhibit self-control and self-discipline. Here is a key thought on this. When you think of the root word of discipline, what other word – a biblical word – shares the same root?"

"Disciple?"

"Exactly, and what is a disciple? A person who follows the teaching of another. So what do you think is the importance, from God's perspective, on us being self-disciplined?"

"For us to show that we are followers of His teachings, true disciples?"

"Right again. You are quick! We discipline ourselves to His teachings, and that, to God, is very important. So every Christian ought to be self-disciplined, and not just in 'spiritual' things like prayer and Bible study. All of our life is spiritual. Our relationships are spiritual. Our finances are spiritual. Our work is spiritual. So when we discipline ourselves in whatever we are doing, we are acting in a spiritual manner. Make sense?"

"Very much so."

"Great. Number four. Time management."

"Time management? That sounds like something Keith should have talked about, being the motivational speaker and all."

"Actually, time management is deeply spiritual. In fact, Ephesians tells us that we should make the most of our time because the days are evil. That is a time management command straight from the Bible."

"Huh, I have never heard that before."

"Yep, check for yourself."

"What does it mean by the days being evil?"

"It simply means that if we don't make the most of our time – or manage it – the days will take over and we will become idle and accomplish nothing. We have to seize our time and consecrate it to God."

"I sure need to learn more about time management. That's for sure. You have any tips?"

"I have lots of tips, but one that is the most important, and it happens to be number five. Mind if we move to that one?"

"No, that sounds great."

"Number five is to live in priority."

"Live in priority?"

"Yes, let me explain. I always think it is funny when people use the word 'priorities' – even when I use it, which I sometimes do – because the word 'priority' means 'the most important.' So, the word can't accurately be pluralized. It is by nature singular. You can have two or three 'most important's.' You can only have one 'most important.'"

"Okay, so how does that fit?"

"It fits this way. The way to manage your time is to always ask yourself this question: At this moment in time, what is the most important thing I could be doing? In other words, *What is my priority?* That is the key to successful time management."

"Just ask myself what my priority should be at every moment?"

"Yes, try it for a week and it will revolutionize your life. Believe me, it will."

"Okay, I will give it a try."

"Great. You know Kate, those five principles: God first, character, self-discipline, time management, and living in priority are found in every single successful person I have ever met. They aren't all perfect, but those traits working together are powerful."

"They sound like it. That certainly gives me food for thought."

"I hope that it has."

"So, will you give Kate and me a tour of the building?"

"I would be happy to. Let's go."

Pastor Farmer gave the ladies a tour of the church building – originally built in 1892 – and recently restored. It was a beautiful old building that had all of the modern amenities inside. It was a testament to the timelessness of the ancient message. The message stays the same even in a modern age.

When they finished the tour, Pastor Farmer excused himself. "I really have to get back to finish my sermon for this Sunday. A few thousand people are counting on me to come up with something to say!"

"We totally understand. Thanks so much for the time, Bill."

"I knew when you asked me for the time, it should be my priority. Now I have to shift and finish my sermon."

Susan and Kate made their way back down to the front door of Susan's building and stopped there for a quick chat before Kate left. "Well, there you have five of my friends."

"Yep. It was great." There was a bit of awkwardness because Kate didn't know how the relationship would go forward from here.

"Kate, I want to meet one more time. Just you and me next week. Same time work for you?"

"Sure, I would love that."

"Great. I will see you next week and we can wrap some things up."

"Okay, I will see you next week."

9

Success Breeds Success

"God has big plans for you."

When Kate entered Susan's office a week later, she could tell something was different but didn't look closely enough to tell exactly what it was. Susan, as always, warmly welcomed her. "Good morning, Kate. How was the week?"

"Great. I had another 'date' with Cory. How was yours?"

"Fantastic."

"Thanks so much for meeting with me again. I didn't know what would happen after you had introduced me to your friends."

"Oh, I am not through with you, as you will see. Let's sit down."

"Okay." They sat on the big overstuffed couches. It was surprising to Kate that a living room set could feel so good, even in a large office.

"Kate, I want to tell you a little more about my story."

"That would be wonderful."

"When I was about thirty, I was a little like you. I wanted so much out of life and yet I didn't now how to get there. I was a Christian and had some of the same questions that you have, and to make it worse, back then, women weren't really as accepted in the workplace as they are now. So an ambitious person, let alone a woman, was a little strange in the church at the time. But my life changed when I met a woman named Caroline Cox. Have you ever heard of her?"

"I think so. It sounds familiar."

"Caroline was a matriarch of Seattle. She and her husband built many businesses here in Seattle. They were charitable, both in the church as well as other areas, like the arts--really tied into the community. Well, long story short, Caroline took me under her wing and taught me just about everything I know. She opened doors for me that I would have never been able to open for myself. She really made me what I am today. Other than God, I owe my life to a strong Christian woman named Caroline Cox."

"Wow. That is amazing. I never knew."

"That's the story behind the story, as they say."

"And quite a story. I guess there is no such thing as a self-made person."

"No there isn't, Kate. We all help one another along in this life, and it is the job of those of us who are along in age to pass along our wisdom and resources to those who come behind us. So, I have a proposition for you."

"You do?"

"Yes, I do. Come with me." Susan got up and walked over to another part of the room. As they walked closer to the group of corner windows facing northwest toward the Puget Sound and the Space Needle, Kate recognized what was different: There was another office set up in the corner. Susan's office remained where it was though, facing southwest toward Puget Sound and Mt. Rainier. "You will notice some changes here."

"Yes, you have another office set up."

"That office is for you Kate. That is, if you want it."

"Well, Susan, I am flabbergasted. I mean, what would I do?"

"Kate, you told me that you worked for Smith, Allen, and Jones when we first met. Do you remember?"

"Sure."

"Larry Smith was my brother's best friend growing up. He was the best man in his wedding. I have known him since before the beginning of time."

"Oh?"

"So I called him up and got your story. He thinks the world of you, Kate, and so do I. So, I want you to come to work for me."

"Okay, but again, what will I do?"

"You leave that to me. I am going to personally mentor you and help you. We will work together and you will learn everything I know. This is my way of paying back Caroline Cox for what she did for me. Down the road, you can do the same for another young woman. Deal?"

"Okay. I am not even going to think about it. I'll take it. When do I start?"

"One week from today. Just show up and I'll take it from there."

"All right then. Wow. I am stunned."

"Don't be. God has big plans for you. You are limited only by yourself. Just let God take you where He wants you. I mean, think about how your life has transpired over a chance meeting on that bus. Now, five weeks later, you have dined with a Senator, flown with a billionaire, you have been on two dates with a quarterback in the NFL and you have a brand new job. You never bargained for that when you showed your bus pass that morning, did you?"

"I certainly didn't."

"Kate, you were made in the image of God, and I believe that I should help you live that out and be His reflection in all that you do. If I can help you do that, I would be eternally grateful for the opportunity."

"Susan, you are too kind."

The phone rang through to Susan's desk. "Oh, that is a phone meeting with my VP in New York. I have to take it. See you next week – say 8:00 am?"

"Done deal. I'll see you then."

The two women hugged and then Susan walked briskly to her phone and picked it up. Kate stood over her new desk. She was astonished at the good fortune she was finding. After a few moments, she walked back to the elevator that would take her downstairs. As she passed the receptionist, she heard, "Congratulations."

Turning back to the receptionist, she beamed. "Thank you. I am so excited."

"See you next week."

"Yes, we will be seeing a lot more of each other, won't we?"

"We sure will. I look forward to it, Kate."

Kate stepped into the elevator and just as the doors were closing, she looked back at the receptionist and again smiling from ear to ear, said, "Me too!"

Chris Widener
THE LEADER of a New Generation of
Personal Development and Leadership Experts

 *Chris Widener is an example of how anyone can overcome any odds to achieve a successful life and help others achieve the same. Chris has overcome many obstacles... living through his father's sudden death when he was four, being sent away from his family to live with relatives at age nine and becoming involved with drugs and alcohol by the age of twelve.*

Chris overcame those obstacles and has been speaking professionally since 1988 and has shared the stage with US Presidential candidates, nationally known television news anchors, best-selling authors and professional athletes. He has spoken on motivation and leadership to some of America's finest organizations such as General Electric, Cisco Systems and the Harvard Business School.

Chris has written over 450 articles, 8 books and has produced more than 30 audio CD programs on leadership and motivation. His articles appear monthly in close to 100 publications.

Chris is also a contributor to The Jim Rohn One-Year Success Plan.

If you would like more information regarding Chris Widener's corporate booking rates go to www.chriswidener.com or email info@chriswidener.com or call 877-929-0439.

To subscribe to Chris Widener's Free Ezine and to see his complete listing of products go to www.chriswidener.com or email widenergroup@gmail.com.

BOOKS BY CHRIS WIDENER

• • • •

THE ANGEL INSIDE

Journey to modern-day Florence, Italy, where a despondent 30-year-old American meets a mysterious old man who challenges him to take a deeper look at his life.

THE ART OF INFLUENCE

A powerful tale that shows that business success does not come from Ivy League degrees, but from an individual's own personal courage and commitment to succeed.

TWELVE PILLARS

This novel by Jim Rohn and Chris Widener will inspire you to take your life to the next level and beyond. It will challenge and encourage you to become the best that you can be!

To order, visit ChrisWidener.com

ABOVE ALL ELSE

The absorbing sequel to Chris Widener and Jim Rohn's best-seller, *Twelve Pillars*. A quick read, an enjoyable story, and one filled with profound insights to help you achieve, sustain, and enjoy your own success.

THE IMAGE

Compelling and to the point, this book addresses questions that so many have struggled to answer in their lives. Chris Widener and his unique ability to weave vital success principles into a story will inspire you to go for it and to reach for your God-given potential!

CHRIS WIDENER'S TREASURY OF QUOTES

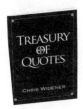

The quotes you'll find in this elegant little book are seeds taken from the collection of articles Chris has written over the years. Read them slowly. Ponder them. Ask yourself how they apply to you. Let the truths you find take root and grow into something magnificent in your life!

Each booklet has a special "To and From" section, making it a great gift for family, friends, and colleagues!

To order, visit ChrisWidener.com

JIM ROHN
DIGITAL PRODUCTS

Find these Jim Rohn digital courses or products at successacademy.com or store.jimrohn.com. All include immediate access and are accessible via a SUCCESS Academy mobile-friendly, password-protected member site.

Foundations for Success (comprehensive 10-module digital course)

The Jim Rohn One-Year Success Plan (52-week course)

Jim Rohn's 90 Days to Financial Mastery (12-week course)

Challenge to Succeed Platinum Collection (8 hours of video, 12 hours of audio, plus workbook and bonuses)

Jim Rohn Seminar Super Library (includes *Excelling in the New Millennium* and *The Weekend Leadership Event*)

For more personal development resources from Jim Rohn, visit store.SUCCESS.com or store.JimRohn.com.

SUCCESS MAGAZINE

SUCCESS

Your supply of new ideas, inspiration, and resources that will continue to give you the competitive advantage in life.
www.SUCCESS.com/subscribe

THE JIM ROHN GUIDE SERIES

The timeless wisdom of Jim Rohn in concise, easy-to-read guides. Perfect for sharing with friends, family, business associates, clients and prospects.

TIME MANAGEMENT
PERSONAL DEVELOPMENT
LEADERSHIP
GOAL SETTING
COMMUNICATION

Quantity discounts available

store.JimRohn.com or store.SUCCESS.com

TWELVE PILLARS AVAILABLE ON KINDLE, NOOK AND APPLE BOOKS!

Read the personal-achievement tour de force by Chris Widener and Jim Rohn on your favorite eReader device.